Here are the Brick Street Boys

Janet and Allan Ahlberg

PictureLions
An Imprint of HarperCollins*Publishers*

Here are the Brick Street Boys.

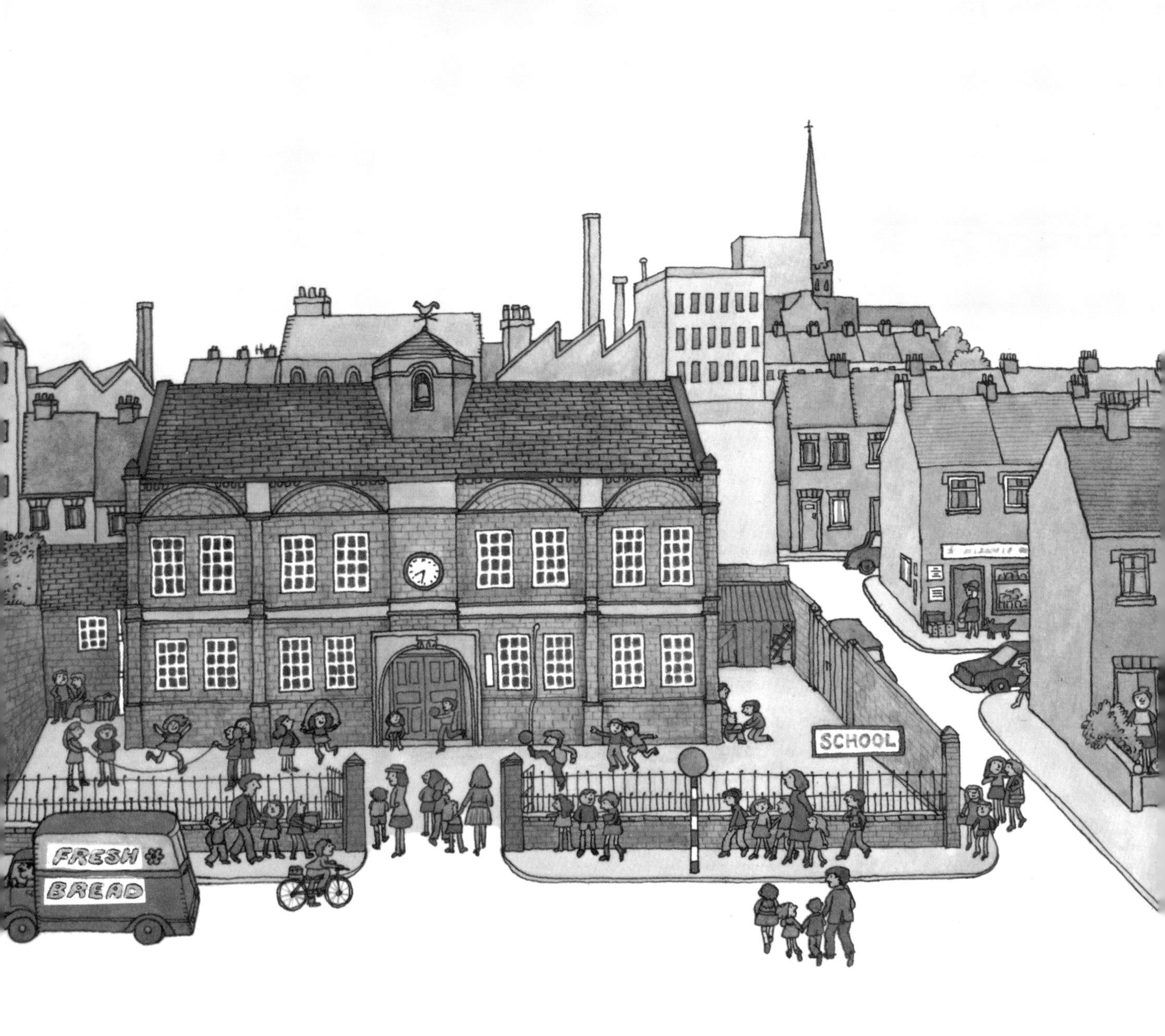

The Brick Street Boys go to Brick Street School.

At school they paint and make up plays.

They write and sing and do their sums.

After school they play football in the playground. They pick two teams – Fred's team and Sam's team.

Here is Fred's team.

Here is Sam's team.

Here is the ball.

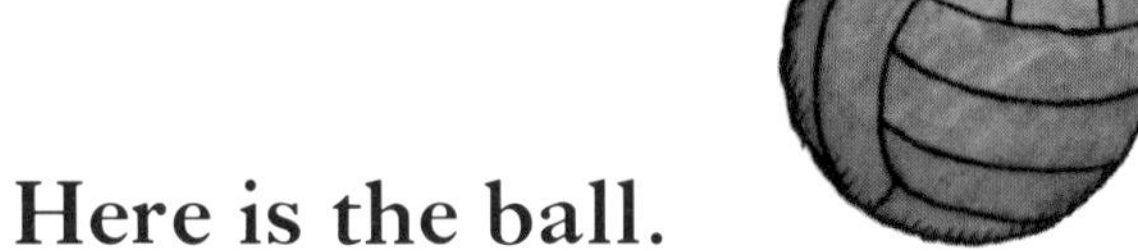

Fred kicks the ball.

Sam kicks the ball.

Fred kicks Sam.

Here is the referee.

The referee talks to Fred.

Fred kicks the referee.

Here is the referee's big brother.
The referee's big brother talks to Fred.

Fred is sent off.

Sam gets ready to take a free kick.

Fred's team make a wall.

Sam passes to Eric. Eric passes to Walter.
Walter passes to Tom. Tom shoots.

Goal! Sam's team is happy.

Fred's team is sad.

Fred is very sad.

Bruce scores a goal.
"Offside," says Fred.

Then Eric scores a goal.
"Foul," says Fred.

Then Sam scores three goals.

"I'm going home," says Fred.
He picks up his coat.

Mr Mott comes into the playground.
He is the football teacher.
"Time to go!" he says.

The referee blows his whistle.
The referee's big brother takes him home.
It is the end of the game.

That night the Brick Street Boys go to bed and dream.
Sam dreams he is scoring lots more goals.

Eric dreams he is scoring lots more goals as well.

Fred dreams he has won the cup

Ambrose dreams he is the best goal-keeper in the world.

First published in Great Britain by
William Collins Sons & Co Ltd 1975
First published in Picture Lions 1992
Picture Lions is an imprint of the Children's
Division, part of HarperCollins Publishers Ltd
77/85 Fulham Palace Road, Hammersmith,
London W6 8JB

Printed by Warners (Midlands) plc,
Bourne + London